MW00655156

A Book of Sanctity

Seton Press
Front Royal, Virginia

Reprinted by Seton Home Study School, 2015

Seton Home Study School
1350 Progress Drive
Front Royal, VA 22630
(540) 636-9990
(540) 636-1602 fax

Internet: www.setonhome.org
E-mail: info@setonhome.org

Front Cover: *Immaculate Conception*

A Book of Sanctity

This book is a collection of stories that have been taken from a variety of sources. The stories are about saints, Old and New Testament Bible heroes, families, and children's adventures. The readers from which they were taken are long since out of print. Unfortunately, we no longer have the originals, and cannot give credit for the sources.

The Little Blue Angel

"Look, Ann," said Jack.
"It is a surprise for you.
It came in the mail.
Is it a birthday gift?"

Jack handed the box to Ann.
"We will see," said Ann.
"Let us take it to Mother."

Then Jack and Ann ran to Mother.

1

Mother was mending socks.
Ann held up the box.
"Look, Mother," she said.
"It just came in the mail.
It is for me.
Father Blain sent it.
Is it a birthday gift for me?"

"Oh," said Ann.
"It is a little blue angel."

"Father Blain sent it as a surprise
for your birthday," said Mother.
"It was good of him to send it."

"Oh, look," said Ann.
"It has real hair."

"The hair is real," said Mother.
"But the rest of it is glass.
Do not drop it.
It may crack."

3

"Here, Ann," said Mother.
"Father Blain sent a note with the angel."

"I will read it," said Ann.
　　"Dear Ann,
　　Here is a birthday gift for you.
　　It has a trick box in it.
　　See if you can find it.
　　I hope you like the gift."

"A trick box!" cried Jack.
"Let me look at it!"

Jack looked for something to press.
He tried and tried to find the box.
Then he gave up.
"I can not find it," he said.
"Here, Ann, you try."

Jack gave the angel back to Ann.
Ann looked and looked at it.
At last she said, "I can not find it.
I can not get the trick box out."

"Let me try," said Pat.
"I will find it."

Pat held the angel in his hands.

He looked and looked for the box.

But he did not find it.

At last Ann said, "We can not
find it, Pat.

I will take it to Mother.

Mother will help us.

She will find the trick box."

Just as Pat handed the angel to Ann
the wings slid down.

A spring clicked.

And a little box came out.

"Oh, good for you!" cried Ann.
"You made the trick box come out, Pat.
And look!
The box has a surprise in it, too.
Father Blain sent me two gifts
for my birthday!"

Saint Blaise

Saint Blaise was a good bishop.
His love of God made him
love his people and be good to them.
He helped them when they
needed help.
People who were sick came
to him and he healed them.
They came and sat at his feet
and he preached to them.

The town had bad men in it.

They did not want to see the good bishop
teaching people to love God.

One day the bad men came to the bishop.

They said, "You must stop preaching
to the people."

"I will not stop," said the bishop.

"God made me.

He died on the cross for me and my people.

I can not stop preaching.

I love God and I will teach my people
to love God, too."

"We will get rid of you," they said.

"We will kill you."

Bishop Blaise did not want to leave
his people.

But the bad men tied him with rope
and led him away.

"Love God," he cried to his people.

"And do not sin.

Pray for me and I will pray for you."

As the bad men led Bishop Blaise
down the street, a mother ran up to them.

"Stop! Stop!" she cried as she fell
at the feet of Bishop Blaise.

The bad men had to stop.

"Bishop Blaise," said the mother.

"A bone is stuck in my little boy's throat and we can not get it out.

Please help him."

The bishop looked at the little boy.

He prayed to God and then blessed the boy's throat.

"Your boy will be safe," he said to the mother.

"Thank you! You have healed him," she said.

"Do not thank me," said the bishop.

"God healed your boy.

You must thank God."

The bad men did not like this.

They struck the mother and made
her and the boy get out of the way.

They led Bishop Blaise out of town
and to the top of a hill.

"We are going to kill you here,"
said one of the men.

The good bishop prayed to God.

He asked God to make him strong.

He asked God to bless and keep his people.

He prayed for the bad men who were going
to kill him.

God helped Bishop Blaise to be brave
and strong.

But at last, the bad men
made him die.

Saint Blaise had spent his life doing good
for others.

He can still help you when you pray to him.

On his feast each year you think
of the way he healed the little boy.

You go to Mass and have your throat
blessed.

When you have a sore throat, it is good
to pray to Saint Blaise.

Saint Martin

It was a chilly day.
Martin and his men rode fast.
"It is late and we must get home.
We will freeze," said Martin.

"No one can stay out long on a day
like this," said one of his men.
"It is good we have
these big thick cloaks."

At last they came to the gates of a town.

A man dressed in rags was standing
near the gates.

"Look!" cried Martin to the other men.

"That man is dressed in rags.

He will freeze on a day like this."

Martin left the others and rode up
to speak to the man in rags.

"What are you going to do?" asked one
of his men.

"This man needs help," said Martin.

"He will freeze.

We must do something to help him."

Martin looked at the man.

His rags were thin and his lips were blue.

"I have no money," said Martin
as he cut his cloak in two.

"But here, take this.

I will share my cloak with you."

Then Martin and his men rode on.

"It was silly to do what you did," one
of his men said to him.

"The man was a tramp."

Martin did not care what others said.

He wished to do what God wanted him to do.

When Martin and the other men reached home, they went to bed.

Martin was just going to sleep when he saw a man standing near his bed.

It was Jesus.

He was dressed like the man Martin had helped.

Jesus looked at him and said, "I was the man you helped at the gate, Martin.

When you do something for people in need, it is the same as doing it for Me."

Martin spent the rest of his life doing good.

When he died the Church made him a saint.

Saint Anthony

One day, Saint Anthony went
to a little town by the sea.

The people in this little town
had a church.

But they did not go to the church
and they did not pray to God.

Saint Anthony wished to tell
these people of God's love.

He wished to tell them that Jesus
died on the cross for them.

But the people did not want to hear him.

One of the men said, "Go away
and do not come back.

We do not want to hear you preach."

"If you will not hear what I have to say,
I will leave you," said Saint Anthony.

"I will go down to the sea and speak
to the fish."

So Saint Anthony left the people and went
to the beach.

In a little while, the people went down
to the beach, too.

They wanted to see what Saint Anthony
was doing.

When they came to the beach, Saint Anthony
was looking at the sea and speaking.

"Come here, big fish and little fish,"
he cried.

"I want to speak to you."

Big and little fish swam up to the shore
near Saint Anthony's feet.

The water seemed to be filled
with splashing fish.

As Saint Anthony spoke, the fish
quit splashing.

"Who gave you the sea for your home?"
he said.

Each of the fish gave a nod.
Saint Anthony went on speaking.
"Yes, God gave you the sea
for your home," he said to them.
"So swim away and praise God.
That is why God made you."

As the fish swam back out to the deep,
deep sea, Saint Anthony lifted his hand
and gave them his blessing.
The people on the beach were filled
with surprise at what they saw.

The people looked at Saint Anthony
for a long time.

Then they cried out to him,
"Please do not leave us.

Teach us to love God as you love Him.

We want to hear what you have to say."

This made Saint Anthony happy.

"Come with me to your church," he said
to them.

"I will teach you about God."

And Saint Anthony led the people
to the church and back to God.

Saint Patrick

When Saint Patrick was a boy,
bad men came to his land.

They tied little Patrick's hands and legs
and sailed away with him on a ship.

The ship sailed for days and days.

At last it reached a land on the other side
of the wide, wide sea.

A rich man paid money for Patrick
and made him a slave.

Patrick's job was to tend
the man's sheep.

While Patrick was tending the sheep,
he did much thinking.

The people of this land did not love God.

They did not have priests to teach them
about God.

As Patrick tended the sheep, he prayed
for these people.

One day, while Patrick was tending the sheep, a man came to him.

"God has sent me to help you," he said to Patrick.

"Run away from here.

A boat is waiting to take you back to your home."

The boat was waiting as the man had said.

Patrick got on the boat and sailed from the land.

For three days the wind and waves tossed the boat.

At last, they reached land and Patrick set out for home.

Patrick was happy to be back home with his father and mother.

But Patrick kept thinking about
the people on the other side of the sea.

One day he spoke to his mother.

"I wish to be a priest," he said.

"As a priest, I can go back
and help those people."

Then Patrick went to see his bishop.

The bishop sent Patrick to school.

Years went by, and at last Patrick
was made a priest.

More years passed and then Patrick
went back to help the people he wanted to help.

One day, Patrick was preaching
to these people about God.

He reached down, picked a little green leaf
and held it up.

"This tells us something about God,"
he said to the people.

"It has three leaves, yet it is one leaf."

In this way he helped to teach the people
about the one true God.

Patrick spent the rest of his life
teaching people about God.

As the years went by, he helped
more and more people to love God.

He spent much time training men
to be priests, too.

Patrick was a wise and good man.

When he died, the Church made him
a saint.

Saint Bernadette

This is about a little girl who saw
the Blessed Mother and spoke to her.

The little girl's name was Bernadette.

Bernadette was a good little girl.

She tried to help her mother
with the chores.

But she was not strong and she
was not well.

One day Bernadette, her sister,
and the girl next door came home from school.

Bernadette's mother was waiting for them.
She said, "Bernadette, will you
and your sister look for dry sticks?
I need them to make a fire."

"I will go, too," said the girl from next door.

So off they ran to find sticks and twigs
for the fire.
They looked down by the creek that ran
past the town.
They hunted for a long time but they
did not find the sticks and twigs they needed.

At last, Bernadette's sister said, "Let us
cross the creek here by the cave.

We will find sticks and twigs
on the other side of the creek."

"You can go," said Bernadette.

"I must stay here and wait for you.

I do not want to get my feet wet
and get sick."

The other girls crossed the creek.

Bernadette sat down to wait for them.

"I will say the rosary while I am waiting,"
she said.

She was saying her rosary when something made her look up.

She looked up at the cave and saw a pretty lady standing in it.

No lady in town was as pretty as this lady.

No one in town had a white dress so pretty as the one this lady wore.

And no one had a sash so blue.

A rose lay on each of the lady's feet.

And a long white rosary hung
from the sash at her waist.

The lady gave Bernadette a smile
and said the rosary with her.

When they came to the end of the rosary,
Bernadette looked up.

The lady was not to be seen.

Three days passed.

Then on the fourth day, Bernadette
went back to the cave.

At the cave, the lady and Bernadette said
the rosary.

The next time Bernadette went to the cave
the lady was waiting for her.

The lady said, "Come here each day
and I will pray with you."

Each day Bernadette went to the cave.

Each day the lady prayed the rosary with her.

One day the lady said to Bernadette,
"Come here.

I have something to tell you."

Bernadette went up to the lady.

"Dig a hole with your hands," said the lady.

Bernadette dug a hole and water gushed out.

One time Bernadette said to the lady,
"Please tell me who you are."

The lady said who she was.
"Please go to the priest," she said.
"Tell him that I want a shrine here.

Tell him that I want people to come here
and pray."

Bernadette did what the Blessed Mother
asked her to do.

Then Bernadette went away to be a nun.

She spent the rest of her life praying
to the Blessed Mother and helping others.

To this day a shrine stands at the cave just as the Blessed Mother wanted.

People come to this shrine each year and pray to her.

People who are sick and lame come, too.

They bathe in the water that comes from the spring.

They hope that God will cure them.

The Angel Cake

"Oh, Bobby! You saw the cake,"
said Bobby's mother.

"I wanted to hide it.

It is a surprise.

Please do not tell the other children
about the cake."

"Why did you bake a birthday cake?"
asked Bobby.

"No one has a birthday this time of the year."

His mother said with a smile, "You will find out
when Father comes home."

Bobby hung up his coat and put
his school things away.

"Can I help you, Mother?" he asked.

"You may scrape the pan," she said.

"You may have the pink frosting that is left."

Bobby cleaned the pan and put it in the sink.

"Mother, is the birthday cake
for one of us?" he asked.

"No, but it is for one who is
near and dear to us," she said.

"You will find out who it is
when we eat."

When Father came home from work,
they sat down to eat.

Near the end of the meal, Mother got up
and went to get the cake.

When the children saw the cake, they said,
"Oh, what a pretty cake!"

"It is a birthday cake," said Bobby.

"And it is an angel cake," said Father.

"Yes," said Mother as she put it down.

"It is an angel cake for the birthday
of the Queen of Angels."

"Oh!" said Bobby.

"It is a birthday cake for the Blessed Mother."

"Do we have a birthday gift for her?"
asked Bobby's little sister.

"We can say a rosary," said Bobby.

"The Blessed Mother will like that," said Mother.

"That will be a fine birthday gift."

A Surprise Map

"Look what my mother gave me!" said Greg.

"It is a map.

Mother said it leads to a surprise."

"I see my house on the map," cried Peter.

"Yes, that is why I am here," said Greg.

"Ask your mother if you may come with me."

Greg and Peter ran to Tom's house.

Tom was fixing his raft.

"Put your things away and come with us,"
said Greg.

"We are going to have fun.

Mother gave me this map and said
that it will lead to a surprise."

Tom jumped up and looked at the map.

"Wait for me!" he cried.

"I'll ask my mother if I may go with you."

The next stop was Sam's store.

"Do you have a surprise for us?" asked Peter.

"Yes," laughed Sam as he handed a box of tacks to Tom.

Then he handed a can of wax to Greg.

And he handed a brush to Peter.

"Sister asked me to give you these things," he said.

"She wants you to bring them to school.

She wants you to help her."

"Sister gave the map to my mother,"
said Greg.

"She is going to let us help her in school.
Come on.
Run as fast as you can."
The boys dashed down the street.
When they reached school, they peeped
in the door.
Sister was painting little chairs with tan paint,
and she had a dab of it on her nose.
The boys laughed.

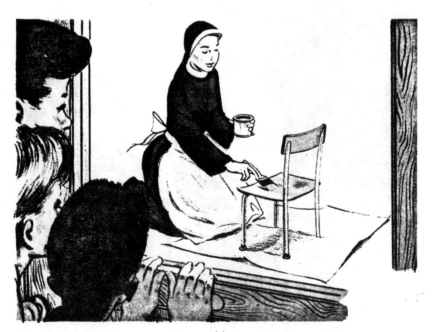

Sister looked up and saw the boys.
"Come in," she said.

"I have lots of work and you boys
can help me."

"It will be fun, Sister," said Greg.

"It is not work when we do things
for you, Sister," said Tom.

Steve's Prize

One day Steve was on his way to school.

As he passed the bank, he saw
a little boy crying.

Steve got off his bike and put it
near a tree.

"Why are you crying?" he asked.

With tears in his eyes, the boy looked up
and said, "I am lost."

"What is your name?" asked Steve.

"Jimmy," said the little boy as a tear
ran down his cheek.

"Do you know the name of your street?"
asked Steve.

"Kent Street," said Jimmy with a sob.

"I wish I had time to take you home,"
said Steve. "But I must be on time for school.

Sister Mary is going to give a prize
to those who are not late for school this year."

He looked at Jimmy.

Jimmy was still crying
and weeping as he hung on
to a little cloth puppy.

By this time, Jimmy
had cried so much that the puppy
looked as if it were crying, too.

"Look, Jimmy," said Steve.

"I will help you get home if you will
stop crying.

I will be late for school and Sister
will not give me a prize.

But I can not leave you here.

Let me see what I can do.

I know it is not safe for two to ride
on a bike.

So I'll leave my bike here.

Give me your hand while we cross the street.

Wipe your eyes and please stop crying."

Just then Father Dell drove past the bank.

He saw the boys and put on his brakes.

"Why, Steve, what are you doing here?"
he asked.

"You will not win a prize if you are late
for school."

"Oh, Father Dell," said Steve.

"This little boy is lost.

I am going to take him home.

I know I am late for school and Sister
will not give me a prize.

But I had to take care of Jimmy."

Father Dell gave Steve a pat on the back.

"You did what Jesus wants us to do,"
he said.

"Jesus wants us to help others.

You may not win a prize at school,

But I know Jesus will bless you
for what you did.

Let me drive Jimmy home, and you go on
to school.

Tell Sister that I will let her know
why you were late."

"Thank you, Father," said Steve
as he got on his bike and rode off to school.

Lucy Sees an Angel

Father Crane was teaching the class
about angels.

"Father, can we see the angels?" asked Frank.

"No," said Father. "But if God lets an angel
take the shape of a man, we can see him."

Let me tell you about three children
who saw an angel."

Lucy was a little girl.

Each day she tended her father's sheep.

The little boy next door and his sister went
with Lucy to take care of the sheep.

They led the sheep out of the town
and up to the top of a hill.

The children prayed the rosary.

Then they played games
while they stayed with the sheep.

One day, while they were tending the flock
of sheep, they saw black clouds in the sky.

"Run to the cave!" cried Lucy.

The children reached the cave
just as the rain came.

"We can keep dry in here, and we can see
the sheep," said Lucy.

While they were in the cave, Lucy said,

"It is time to say the rosary."

"Say it fast then," said the little boy.

"I want to play with stones."

The three children said the rosary.

Then a gust of wind made the children
look out of the cave.

A white cloud floated past the tops
of the trees.

It floated up to the cave.

As it came close to the cave, the children
saw a boy standing in the cloud.

His white robe gleamed like the sun.

He looked at them and said, "Do not fear.

I am an angel.

Pray with me."

The children prayed with the angel.

And this time the little boy wanted to pray.

When the children had prayed, they looked up.

The angel was not to be seen.

The angel came back two other times to pray with the children.

"Pray," he said each time.

"Pray for those people who do not pray.

Do things you do not want to do and do them for God."

From that time on, the children spent each day praying and doing what God wanted them to do.

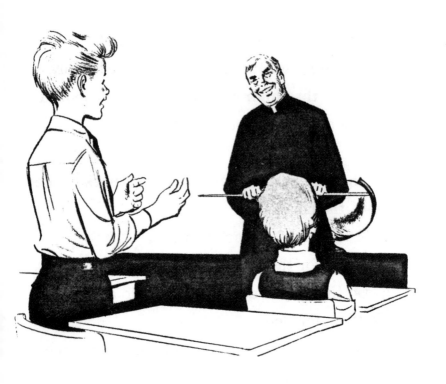

"I like that, Father," said Frank.

"I'm glad you do," said Father Crane.

"But why did the angel come?"

"To tell the children that they must pray," said Frank.

"And try to do each act for God."

"Yes, that is why the angel came," said Father Crane with a smile.

One Good Man

At one time God's people became wicked.
They did not do what God told them to do.
They did not want to think about God.

All they wanted to do was eat, drink, and
have a good time.

When God saw this, He said, "I will kill them,
and with them all the beasts on the land and
all the birds in the air."

But God saw one man who was good.
The man's name was Noe.

God wished to save this one good man.

He said to Noe, "The rest of the people are so wicked that I am going to kill them."

Then God told Noe to make a big boat.

"It must have three decks on it," He said.

"You will line it within and without so that water will not seep in.

You and your sons shall go into the boat.

Take your wife and the wife of each son with you.

And from the beasts and birds and creeping things, take two pair of each, so that they will not die."

Noe did as God told him.

The wicked people laughed at Noe and made fun of his boat.

"We do not fear God," they said.

At last the day came when Noe and his wife went into the boat.

So did each son and his wife.

They had with them every beast and bird that God told Noe to take.

When they were all inside the boat, God shut them in from the outside.

Then it began to rain.

The rain lasted for forty days.

The water rose to the tops of the trees, and then to the tops of the hills.

At last not a bit of land was left to be seen.

And the people and beasts and birds and creeping things that were not in the boat were killed by the waters.

When forty days had passed, the rains began
to stop, but the waters stayed on the land
for one hundred and fifty more days.

The boat came to rest on top of a hill.

The waters were on every side of it.

One day while Noe was waiting for the waters
to go down, he sent out a bird.

The bird soared up into the air, but came back
to the boat.

This told Noe that the land still had water
on it.

Noe waited a week before he sent the bird
back out. This time the bird came back
to the boat, bringing a branch with green leaves
on it.

This told Noe that the land was dry.

Then God told Noe to take every
leave the boat.

When Noe and his sons had everything
off the boat, they gave praise to God and
thanked Him for keeping them safe.

God looked down upon Noe and blessed him
saying, "This is the last time that I shall use
water to kill all men and beasts.

And so that all men will know this, I will
set a rainbow in the sky."

Noe and his sons looked up.

There in the sky was a rainbow.

Feeling safe and happy, Noe and his sons
began to make a home on the dry land.

God's Way

At one time God's people were slaves
in the land of a wicked king.

He was cruel to them and they were not
happy.

One of them was the mother of a little girl
and a baby boy.

One day the little girl asked her mother,
"May I help you take care of the baby?"

"Yes, Mary," said her Mother. "But do not let
any of the king's men see the baby. If they
find him, they will kill him."

One day Mary's mother saw the king's men
in the street.

Quick as a flash she put the baby in a soft blanket
and laid him in a basket. Then she put a cloth
on top of the basket to shade him from the sun.

"This house is too little to hide the baby,
Mary," she said. "Let us take him down
to the Nile and hide him in the reeds."

When they reached the bank of the Nile, Mary's
mother kissed the baby and said, "By the grace
of God, may my little boy be safe."

Then she said to Mary, "Stay near the baby
and play. If any of the king's men come close,
run and let me know."

One day while Mary was playing in the sand
near the baby, the princess and her maids came
down to the Nile to bathe their feet.

Mary saw the princess and her maids walk
down to the water.

As the princess came close to the baby,
Mary's heart began to beat fast.

Then the princess saw the basket. "Why is
that basket floating in the reeds?" she asked one
of her maids. "Go get it for me."

"The basket has a baby in it," said the maid
as she handed the basket to the princess.

Mary sat as still as she could. She did not
know what to do.

The princess lifted the cloth from the basket.

"Why! It is a little baby boy!" she cried. "He must belong to one of the slaves."

Then the princess lifted the baby out of the basket and held him close to her.

"I will take care of you," she said. "I will not let any of my father's men kill you."

"But you cannot take him home with you," said one of her maids.

"No," said the princess. "I will find a slave and pay her to take care of him."

Then Mary ran up to the princess and said, "I know someone who will be glad to take care of the baby. May I go get her?"

"Yes," said the princess. "Bring her to me."

Mary ran as fast as she could to get her mother.

When Mary's mother reached the shore,
the princess said to her, "Take care of this baby
for me. I will pay you for your work and
for the things the baby will need.

His name shall be Moses. That means 'kept
safe from the water.'

When he is big, I will treat him as my son
and have my wise men teach him."

"Moses will be his name," said the mother.
"I will take good care of him."

She thanked God as the princess gave her
the baby.

When Moses was still a little boy,
the princess sent for him.

"Moses, you know I love you as my son,"
she said to him. "Come and stay with me and be
my son.

You will have everything you want, and I will
have my wise men teach you all they know."

In this way, God trained Moses for the work
He wanted him to do.

When Moses became a man, he went back
to his people and led them out of the land
of the wicked king.

Peter and the Angel

Jesus had died on the cross, and Saint Peter was in charge of the Church.

He did what Jesus had told him to do.

He started to teach the people about God and baptize all who came to him.

He did other things, too.

He asked the people to love God and to love one another.

But Herod was still king, and Herod was
a wicked man.

"I know what I will do," he said to himself.
"I will order my men to find Peter and put him
in jail.

I have killed James for teaching about Jesus.
And I will kill Peter, too!"

So Herod sent for his men and said,
"I order you to find Peter and put him
in jail.

Chain his hands and feet, and do not let
him get away!

I have killed other men.

After the feast, I will send for Peter,
and I will kill him, too."

The king's men did as they were ordered.
Then four of them stayed with Peter while
the others stayed outside the jail.

Hearing that Peter was in chains, his people
prayed and prayed for him.

Four days passed and Peter was still in jail.

One of the men at last spoke to Peter.

"This is your last day in jail, Peter," he told him laughing. "The king will kill you in the morning. Your God cannot save you from the king!"

"We shall see," said Peter. "I trust in the Lord. The Lord can do what He wants with me."

Then all of the men mocked Peter and laughed at him. But Peter did not care.

At last Peter went to sleep between two of the men in charge of him.

As he slept, an angel of the Lord came to him.

The angel struck Peter on the side and woke him, saying, "Get up, Peter!"

At once the chains fell from his hands.

Then the angel said to him, "Dress yourself and put on your shoes."

Peter did as the angel told him to do.

Then the angel said, "Put on your cloak and come with me!"

The men who were with Peter in the jail did not see the angel. They did not see Peter get up.

The angel led Peter past the king's men and outside the jail.

They came to the big gate leading into the city.

The gate opened by itself.

Then the angel walked with Peter down a street of the city. And all of a sudden, the angel left him.

Peter thanked God for sending an angel to save him from Herod.

Next, Peter went to the house of Mary,
the mother of Mark.

The house was filled with people who had come
there to pray for Peter.

Peter went up to the first door and began
to rap. "Open the door!" he cried.

The girl who came to the door of the house
did not open it but ran back to the people
inside.

"Peter is standing outside!" she cried.

But the people said to her, "You are mad.
You have seen Peter's angel!"

But at last, hearing Peter, the people
ran to the door.

"It is Peter! It is Peter!" they cried.

They led him into the house, and Peter told them
about the angel who had come to save him.

The next morning the men in charge of Peter could not find him.

"What has become of him?" they cried. "The chains were on him when he went to sleep. The king will kill us if we cannot find him."

They looked here and there, but they could not find Peter.

When the sun came up, the king himself came to the jail.

"Bring Peter to me at once!" he ordered.

"Peter is not in the jail," said one of the men. "We cannot find him."

King Herod was angry. He had the men killed that day.

But the angel had freed Saint Peter from the wicked king, and he was safe and far away.

The Best Way

Father Ford rang the bell at Nora's home.

As he waited on the porch, he could hear Nora speaking to her mother in the kitchen.

"I know it is my turn to sweep the floor," Nora was saying.

"But I do not like to work.

I wish I were a squirrel or a bird or a rabbit.

Then I would not have to work, and I could be happy!"

When Nora saw who was on the porch,
she said, "Oh, good morning, Father. Please
come in."

"Good morning, Nora," said Father Ford.
"I could hear what you were saying to your mother.
Come out and see the pretty squirrel on the grass.
Have you ever asked him why he is happy?"

Nora began to smile.

"Oh, Father, that would be silly,"
she said. "A squirrel cannot speak."

Just then the squirrel sat up and looked
at them.

"What makes you happy, little squirrel?" asked
Father Ford.

The squirrel said, "I am doing what
God wants me to do. That is why I am happy."

Then he picked up a nut.

With a whirl and a twirl, he was up
in a tree.

Nora's eyes opened wide in surprise.

Father Ford and Nora went into the house.

"I will tell Mother that you are here," said Nora.

"Sh! Stand still!" said the priest.

"I want to ask your little bird something."

Then he said, "What makes you so happy, little yellow bird?"

The little bird said, "I am singing. And that is what God wants me to do. That is why I am so happy!"

Then it started to sing once more. It sang and sang and sang.

"Oh, Chirpy, you never spoke like that before," said Nora.

Just then Nora's mother came in.

"You may go outside with Tom," she said
to Nora.

Nora went out to the backyard and saw Tom
feeding his rabbits.

"Oh, Tom," she said. "Can your rabbits talk?
A squirrel and Chirpy talked for Father Ford."

Then she told Tom what had happened.

Tom laughed and said, "Father Ford was doing
the talking for the squirrel and Chirpy.

He was saying what they would tell you if
they could think and speak."

Nora walked to the front of the house and
sat on the steps.

She began to think.

When Father Ford came out of the house
Nora said, "Oh, Father! Tom told me that
you did the talking for the squirrel and Chirpy.
But I think I know why you did it."

The priest smiled at the little girl and
said, "I think you know, too, Nora.

The squirrels and the birds do what God wants
them to do, and they are happy.

If a little girl would do what God wants
her to do, she would be happy, too."

Then Nora asked, "Who will tell that little girl
what God wants, Father?"

The priest said, "When you do what your
father or mother tell you to do, you are
doing what God wants."

Then Nora smiled her best smile and said,
"I'll try to do what God wants me to do, Father."

The Saint of Little Children

Once there was a little boy named Joseph
Sarto.

When he was small, everyone liked to call him
"Beppo." The name seemed to fit him very well.

Beppo's father and mother had a house in a small
town. They worked hard every day, but still they
were very poor.

Beppo worked hard, too, helping his father and
mother with the smaller children.

The priest of the village liked to visit the village school. He liked to help the children with their work. He liked to talk to them.

One day, when he was visiting the school, he stopped at Beppo's desk.

"You do very good work in school, Beppo," he said.

"School is very easy, Father," said Beppo.

"Would you like to come to me each day after school?" asked the priest. "I will help you learn more about God and His Church."

Beppo smiled and said, "Yes, Father, I should like to very much."

So every day Beppo went to the priest's house.

One day as he was leaving for home, he said, "Father, I want to become a priest, but I know my father needs my help. We are very poor."

The good priest said, "Beppo, if God wants you to become a priest, He will help you. Pray to Our Blessed Mother every day."

A long time passed. Then the priest went to see Beppo's father and mother.

"I have come to talk to you about Beppo," he said. "He is praying that God will let him become a priest. But he thinks that you will need him at home."

Beppo's father and mother looked at each other. "What do you think about it, Father?" they asked.

The priest spoke. "I really think that God wants Beppo to become a priest," he said.

Then Beppo's father said softly, "It shall be as you say, Father. God will take care of us."

His mother did not say anything. She raised her eyes and thanked God.

Beppo left home and went away to be a priest. Years went by. When he came back, the people no longer called him "Beppo." When they spoke to him, they called him "Father Sarto."

Father Sarto was a very good priest.

All the children loved him very much and
liked to be with him.

One day he saw a little girl sitting on a doorstep
crying.

"My little one," he said gently as he sat down
beside her. "Why are you crying?"

"My doll lost her arm, and I cannot get it back
on," said the little girl.

"Maybe I can help you," said the priest. He
reached for the doll and began to mend it.

In a little while it was fixed. "Dry your eyes,
my little one," he said. "See, the doll is fixed."

The little girl looked up at the priest. "Oh,
thank you!" she said as she hugged her doll.

One day Father Sarto was teaching a class of older boys and girls.

They were going to receive Our Lord into their hearts for the first time.

While Father Sarto was teaching, a little boy came into the church. He quickly sat down with the other children.

When class was over, he went up to Father Sarto. "Father, may I receive Our Lord, too?" he asked. "I know that the host is Jesus. I know everything that you have told the bigger boys and girls."

Father Sarto looked sadly at the boy. "No, my little one," he said. "You must wait another six years. Someday, maybe the Pope will let little children like you receive Our Lord. I hope so."

Before long, Father Sarto was made a bishop.

Then later he became Pope. He was called Pope Pius the Tenth.

As Pope, one of the first things he did was to ask that little children receive Our Lord at Mass.

"When little children understand that the Host at Mass is really Jesus, they may receive Him into their hearts," he said.

So after this, little children in all lands could receive Our Lord.

Little Beppo, who became Pope Pius the Tenth, died a saint. People call him the Saint of Little Children.

The Beasts God Chose

It was a clear cold night, and the sky was filled with stars.

Two people were still on the road. A man was leading a small gray donkey. On it was a lovely lady.

Shepherds, as they tended their sheep on a faraway hill, saw them.

The shepherds had a strange feeling that this night would not be the same as other nights. They felt that something was going to happen.

Some beasts in a nearby cave seemed to sense something in the air, too.

An ox smelled the fresh yellow hay that was left for him in the crib. But he would not eat it. He lay down on the floor and looked at a mother sheep and her two baby lambs.

They began to bleat softly. Then they walked over to the big ox and lay down close to his side.

Two pretty white birds stopped singing and sat very still.

All of the beasts seemed to be waiting—waiting for something to happen.

Then in the stillness of the night, they could hear the clip-clop of the little donkey's feet.

The little donkey was coming closer and closer.

The big ox began to breathe more quickly.

The sheep and the lambs blinked their eyes and looked at the door of the cave.

The two white birds sat closer to each other and waited.

In a little while, the man leading the donkey came
into the cave and held up a lamp to see.

"Oh, good beasts, will you give me some of your
hay?" he asked. "This night we will have need of it.
This night a Child will be born."

The ox and sheep got up on their feet and walked
away from the hay.

The man picked up an armful of hay and made a bed
on the floor. Then he went to get the lovely lady
and bring her into the cave.

As the beasts saw her, a restful peace came
over them, and they went to sleep.

After a while, the man turned down the lamp, but he did not go to sleep. He had to see that no harm would come to the lady.

Everything was peaceful and quiet.

Then all at once the little gray donkey pricked up his ears. And the other beasts began to stir.

They could see a star shining into the cave.

They could hear angels singing in the night.

THEN THEY SAW THE BABY!

He was lying in the crib. The lovely lady and the good man were beside Him.

At first, the beasts stayed to one side.

Then the gray donkey and the ox walked over to the crib. They looked down at the Baby and tried to keep the cold night air away from Him.

The sheep and the lambs crept close to the lovely lady.

The little white birds sang softly.

The shepherds came one by one into the cave.

The lovely lady held the Baby up for all to see.

She said, "Jesus has come to all of us. Come and adore Him."

Peter's Christmas Gift

A week before Christmas, Peter came home
from school and walked into the kitchen.

He saw Barbara working with Timmy and Jean.

Paint and glue, scraps of paper and cardboard
were all over everything.

"What are you doing?" asked Peter.

"We are making Christmas gifts for Mother and
Father," said Barbara.

"Look at my letter box," said Jean.

"Look at my letter box," said Timmy.

"What are Mother and Dad going to do with two letter boxes?" asked Peter.

"Put mail in them. What do you think?" asked Timmy.

Everyone laughed. Then Barbara looked at Peter. "What do you have, Peter? I guess you went down to the store and got something," she said.

"I make my gifts every year," said Peter. "But not this year. And I'm not going down to the store for one, either!"

"You should have something," said Barbara. "You can work here with us, if you want to. Mother said she would not come in until it is time for supper."

"No, thank you," said Peter. "Do you think I want to get paint and glue all over me?"

Barbara kept thinking as she worked. "Peter has a gift," she said to herself. "He is just teasing me. I'll find his hiding place."

She looked upstairs and downstairs. But she could not find a thing.

Every day Barbara kept asking Peter if he was teasing her. Peter was careful. Never once did he say that he was not teasing her.

But really he was.

Every night after supper, the same thing happened. Barbara would hear him ask Mother if he could go over to Grandmother's.

Barbara did not know what he did when he got there. Grandmother would take some papers and sit down. Peter would stand in front of her and talk and talk.

If Peter ever stopped, Grandmother would quickly look at the papers. Then she would get Peter started again.

Barbara was certainly going to be surprised this Christmas!

Christmas came at last.

Father and Mother and the children were
on their way home from Mass.

"Get your gifts for Mother and Father," said
Barbara to the others. "I'll put them under the
tree."

"You cannot put mine under the tree," said Peter
teasing her.

"You mean you do not have anything for Mother
or Father?" asked Barbara.

"I do not have anything for you to put under
the tree," said Peter smiling.

"I'm surprised at you, Peter," said Barbara.
"What will Mother and Father think?"

When they reached home, Timmy, Jean, and Barbara went to get their gifts. Peter just waited with Father and Mother.

Barbara put the gifts under the tree.

"Merry Christmas!" said Father.

"Merry Christmas!" said everyone.

Then they went over to the tree. Timmy picked up a little red car and tried to make it run. Jean hugged a big doll she saw under the tree.

"These ice skates are just what I wanted," said Barbara.

Peter held on to a big bike and pressed gently on the horn.

Then Barbara put her ice skates down. She looked at her mother and father. "We have gifts for you," she said. "That is, some of us do." She looked at Peter and smiled.

Barbara gave her gift first.

"What a beautiful gift!" said Father. "I can use a nice tie rack like this."

"Thank you for the purse," said Mother. "It is very beautiful."

Then Timmy gave Father his letter box. "Mine is bigger," he said.

"Thank you, Timmy," said Father. "It is the biggest letter box I have ever seen!"

Jean gave Mother the letter box she made. "Mine is a little longer," she said.

"I like it," said Mother. "It is beautiful."

Then everyone looked at Peter.

Peter felt funny. He put his head down.

At last he spoke. "Mother and Dad, I have
a gift for you, too. But it is not like the others."

Just then the doorbell rang.

"It's Grandmother," yelled Timmy.

Everyone rushed to the door.

"You are just in time, Grandmother," said Peter.

"Come in," said Father. "You told us you were
going down to the farm. What happened?"

"I missed my train," said Grandmother. "I will
feel more at home here, anyway."

"This will be a nice Christmas for all of us!"
said Mother. "I'm glad you missed the old train!"

"And so am I," said Peter to himself.

Grandmother sat down with Mother and Father.

Timmy and Jean and Barbara began to play on the floor near the tree.

But not Peter. He was standing in front of his father and mother and grandmother.

"I can give you my gift," he said. "But please tell Timmy and the girls to be quiet."

Grandmother winked at Peter. He said, "My gift for Father and Mother is a poem about Christmas. Grandmother helped me learn it."

Then Peter began to say the poem. It was a long and beautiful one.

He said all of it. He did not forget a line.

When he came to the end, everyone clapped.

"That is a beautiful gift, Peter," said Mother.

"It was a long poem to learn," said Father.

"I like it," said Timmy.

"So you were teasing me, Peter," said Barbara. "You had a gift all the time. And it was one I could not put under the tree."

"For a while I did not think that I had a gift at all," said Peter. "I forgot the poem and could not say it."

Peter smiled. "Then Grandmother came with the papers and helped me say it."

"I did not help you say it at all, Peter," said Grandmother. "I do not have the poem."

Then Grandmother turned to the others. "The poem is over at my house. These are just some old papers I had in my purse!"

"What a nice Christmas," said Mother. "I like all of the gifts. They are much nicer than the ones you get at the store."

My Gift to God

Dear God, please take and keep
Each thing that I do this day—
My work, my play, my sleep,
The things that I do and say.

Please take, dear God, these things
That I hear and feel and see.
Take them, O King of Kings!
I hope that they please Thee.

99

St. Margaret Mary

One day when St. Margaret Mary was a little girl, she was praying in church.

Two other little girls were playing outside.

"I wish Margaret Mary would play with us," said one of the girls.

"She is making a visit," said the other girl. "When she comes out, let's ask her to play."

The girls did not have to wait long. Margaret Mary came out, and they asked her to play.

"I'd like to for a while," she said. "Then I'll have to go home and help my mother."

When Margaret Mary played, she played as hard as she could. She played fair and kept the rules.

When Margaret Mary worked, she worked hard. She did everything that she was told to do. And she did it well.

"God wants me to do these things," she would say with a smile. "I am doing them for God."

Many times a day she would speak to God and say, "You made me, dear God. I belong to You. Help me to do everything for You."

After some years passed, Margaret Mary became
a Sister. As a Sister she had more ways of doing
things for God.

Then one day while she was praying, Our Lord came
to her.

She raised her head and saw Our Lord standing
in front of her. He looked very sad.

"Look at My Heart," He said.

Sister Margaret Mary looked at Our Lord's Heart.
It seemed to be on fire. Flames were coming from It.

"This is the Heart that has loved people so much,"
He said. "But people do not think of Me or love Me."

"I want you to do something for Me."

Jesus then told Sister Margaret Mary that every sin hurts His Sacred Heart. He wanted her to ask good people to make up for the sins of others. People should offer up their good works to Him.

Jesus told Sister Margaret Mary that if people did as He asked them to do, they would receive many blessings from Him.

Sister Margaret Mary spent the rest of her life giving this message to the people. She wanted everyone to love the Sacred Heart of Jesus.

Many people offer everything they do each day to the Sacred Heart of Jesus for the sins of men.

In this way every time they do something good, they do it for God.

After Sister Margaret Mary died, the Church made her a saint.

Lucy Sees the Lady of Light

One day Father Crane came to see the class.

"Some time ago," he said, "I told you about three children who saw an angel."

Frank raised his hand. "Do you mean Lucy and the little girl and boy who helped her take care of her father's sheep?"

"Yes," said Father Crane. "Later on they saw our Blessed Mother. Let me tell you about it."

Lucy and the other two children went out every
day to take care of the sheep. They saw the angel
two more times. Just as before, he told them to pray
and to keep praying.

The children did so. They said their rosary every
day after lunch.

One day after they had said their rosary, they
wanted to play.

"Let's make a house," said the little boy. "I
know where we can find some big stones."

"That will be fun," said Lucy. "Come on, run!"

As the children began to run, they saw a flash
of light in the sky.

"It can't be a storm," said Lucy. "The sky is clear."

Then they saw another flash of light and they looked up. Lucy and the other little girl saw a lovely Lady.

The Lady was dressed in white and gold.

She was standing on a cloud just over a stubby tree.

She spoke to the children. "Do not be afraid," she said. "I will not hurt you."

Lucy went a little closer. "Where did you come from?" she asked.

"I am from heaven," said the Lady.

"What do you want of me?" asked Lucy.

"I want you to come here on the thirteenth day of each month. I want you to do this for the next six months. Then I will tell you who I am and what I want," said the Lady smiling.

The little boy looked at Lucy. "You are speaking to someone," he said. "Who is it? I do not see or hear anyone."

Lucy told this to the Lady.

"Tell him to say his rosary," said the Lady.
"Then he will see me."

Lucy told the little boy, and he began to say the
rosary. As he did so, he saw the Lady.

"Will each of you give yourself to God?" asked
the Lady. "Will each of you take the sufferings He
sends you? Will you do this for sinners?"

"Yes," said Lucy.

"Say the rosary every day," said the Lady. With
this, she rose into the air, and the children could
see her no longer.

The children agreed to tell no one about the Lady.

But one of them forgot. In no time at all, everyone had heard about the Lady.

Many of the people said, "It's the Blessed Mother!" Others said, "The children are telling lies!"

On the thirteenth of June, the children went out again to see the Lady. This time many people went with them.

The children saw the Lady, but the people could not. All they saw was a white cloud hanging over the stubby little tree.

For the next three months, the children went out to see the Lady. Again and again she said, "Say the rosary. Pray for sinners."

Then came the sixth month. People came from everywhere to be with the children. It was a day the children would never forget.

As the people waited they saw the sun begin to whirl in the sky. It seemed to leave the sky and come zig-zagging down at them.

Someone screamed, "God have mercy on us!"

The people saw the sun come down until it reached the treetops. Then it stopped.

In the meantime the children saw the Lady of Light. She was standing on one side of the sun. The Child Jesus and Saint Joseph were standing on the other side.

Then the sun rose back into the sky and the visit was over.

"The children have not lied," said the people looking at the faces of the children. "They have seen our Blessed Mother."

After that many of them led better lives. They began to do the things that Lucy told them the Lady of Light wanted them to do.

Saint Dorothy

Once in a while Father Crane read a story to the boys and girls in second grade.

One day he said, "This is the feast of Saint Dorothy. Would you like to hear a story about her?"

"Yes, Father!" cried all the children.

Father Crane took a big heavy book from the desk. "This story is a legend," he said. "A legend is a story that may or may not be true."

He opened the book and began to read.

A long time ago in a faraway land, lived a
lovely young girl. She loved God very much and
tried to lead a life that would please Him. This
young girl's name was Dorothy.

The land in which she lived had many false
gods. It was ruled by a very mean and
wicked man.

He made the people adore the false gods.

"Adore our gods," he said, "or I will put you
to death!"

Dorothy loved the one true God. She did not
care what the wicked ruler said or did.

"I will give my life for Jesus," she said.
"I am not afraid."

111

One day the wicked ruler heard about Dorothy.
He became angry.

"Go find Dorothy, and bring her to me," he
told his men. "I will make her adore our gods
and burn incense before them."

It was not hard for the men to find Dorothy.
They took her from her home and led her
to the ruler.

The ruler smiled at her and said, "Dorothy,
you are a very lovely young girl. I wouldn't want
anything to happen to you. Take some incense and
burn it before our gods."

Dorothy did not raise her head. She did not
say a word.

"Come, Dorothy," said the ruler. "Take a little
incense and burn it. It will not hurt. Nobody
will know."

A feeling of deep peace came over Dorothy.

"No," she said. "God knows everything that
we do. Jesus is my Lord, my Master, and my God.
Him, and Him alone, do I love."

Dorothy could see that the ruler was growing very angry.

"Forget about Jesus," he cried. "Don't let me hear His name again!"

Then he rose from his chair. He walked over to her and looked down at her. "Burn the incense before our gods," he cried. "This is your last chance! Burn the incense or I will have my men put you to death!"

Dorothy looked at him. "I am ready to die for Jesus," she said. "Kill me. Kill me if you must, for then I will go to heaven and be with Jesus."

The ruler turned to his men. "Take her away!" he screamed. "Take her away and put her to death!"

The men led Dorothy away. They led her down a
street. People stopped to look at her. Some of
them were crying. Others were laughing at her
and making fun of her.

"Dear Jesus," she prayed raising her eyes to
heaven. "Give me the grace to be brave. Help
the people who are laughing at me and mocking me."

A young man wanted to tease her. "Dorothy!
Dorothy!" he called out. "When you get to
heaven, think of me. Send me some fruit and
some roses!"

Dorothy turned and looked at him. "Yes," she
said sweetly and softly, "I will when I
get to heaven."

Then the ruler's men led her on to a place
where they put her to death.

That evening, the young man was eating with his friends. He told them about teasing Dorothy. "And guess what!" he said. "She told me that she would send the fruit and roses."

He began to laugh, and his friends began to laugh with him. But suddenly they stopped.

There, at the young man's side, stood an angel. The angel held a silver tray. On it were fruit and roses. The angel looked at the young man and said, "Dorothy sends these to you."

The young man's heart nearly stopped beating. "Dorothy's God is the true God," he said.

From that time on, the man loved God. Soon, he himself was put to death by the same ruler.

First Communion Day

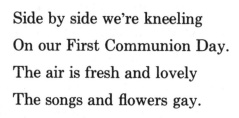

Side by side we're kneeling
On our First Communion Day.
The air is fresh and lovely
The songs and flowers gay.

The candles on the altar
And the little golden bell
Join us in our happiness
And try our joy to tell.

Angels are around us—
I can almost feel them near.
The Saints and Mother Mary
Are surely present here.

Help me, Mother Mary,
Welcome Jesus to my heart.
Tell Him that I love Him
And help me do my part.

Tracks in the Snow

Rocco Bunny peeped out of the rabbit hole. A few flakes of snow fell softly on his bunny nose. Snow was something new to Rocco Bunny.

"Come back here, Rocco Bunny," called Mother Rabbit. "I want to talk to you little bunnies."

Soon Rocco was at the head of a line of five little rabbits.

"I just saw a wolf in the woods next to us," said Mother Rabbit. "He likes rabbit stew, so be very, very careful. If you see his tracks in the snow, find out which way he is going. Then run the other way as fast as you can."

"I don't know what a wolf's tracks look like," said Rocco Bunny. "I've never seen snow before."

"Oh, that's right," said Mother Rabbit. "Come bunnies. You will have to learn a thing or two."

Just then Rocco saw something dart past the rabbit hole. "What was that, Mother?" he asked.

"We'll find out," she said. She led the bunnies out into the snow to look at the tracks. "The front foot has four toes, and the hind foot has five toes," she said. "It was a big squirrel that ran past our place just now."

"You can tell from the tracks which way he was going, can't you?" asked Rocco.

"Yes," said his mother. "And you can tell how fast he was going, also."

"If I would follow the tracks, I'd soon catch up to the squirrel, wouldn't I?" asked Rocco.

"Yes," said Mother Rabbit. "But you'd have to be very fast."

Rocco began following the tracks. Soon he saw some small tracks. "What are these?" he called to Mother Rabbit.

"Mice tracks," she said as soon as she saw them.

"Look! They are following the squirrel's tracks," said Rocco.

Suddenly, Mother Rabbit pricked up her ears and stood very still. Rocco saw her do this and knew that something was wrong.

"I hope it's the mean old wolf," said Rocco to himself. "I'd like to see him." He began to run back to Mother Rabbit.

"Freeze!" called his mother. In rabbit talk that means to stand still right where you are. All the bunnies stood still, even Rocco.

He looked at the ground near his mother and saw why she had stopped.

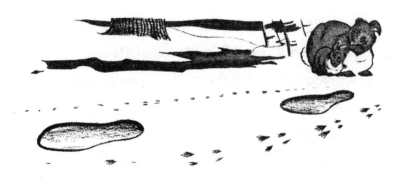

There were two huge tracks in the snow. They
did not look like the other tracks. They were
much bigger, and they were very flat and plain.

Mother Rabbit knew that she had never seen
anything like them before.

Rocco began running ahead. "Here are some
more new ones," he called back.

"Those are deer tracks," said Mother Rabbit
catching up with him. "Deer won't hurt you. But
I am afraid of those other tracks. They look
so strange."

"I'm not afraid," said Rocco and he began
running and following the tracks up the hill.

"Come back," called his mother. But Rocco did
not hear her. He dashed ahead following the
tracks to the top of the hill.

When Rocco was almost to the top of the hill, he turned around and waited for Mother Rabbit and the other little bunnies.

Then they all hopped to the top of the hill. Rocco, of course, was the first one to reach the top. As he did so, he stopped suddenly and cried, "Look down there!"

At the foot of the hill they could see a little house. All kinds of animals were sitting quietly in front of it. A man was talking to them.

The man wore a brown robe with a white cord around the waist. He wore sandals on his feet.

"It's Francis!" said Mother Rabbit. "My grandfather told me about him. He is the friend of all the animals. Look! Even the wolf is there."

This was all that Rocco needed to know. He drew back his ears, leaped into the air, and raced down the hill.

St. Francis saw Rocco coming. "Come, Brother Rabbit," he said. "You, too, have been made by God."

As Rocco came close to the Saint, he saw more and more of the plain, flat tracks in the snow. Then he looked at the Saint's feet. The strange tracks had been made by the Saint's sandals.

A flock of birds flew down over the animals and up to the Saint. St. Francis threw crumbs to them.

Then Rocco Bunny saw the Saint raise his hand in blessing. He heard him say, "Little sisters and brothers, praise God and love Him!"

The Easter Candle

"Surprise! Surprise!" shouted Joseph as he opened the door of his grandfather's shop. His grandfather was a candlestick maker.

"So it's my Joseph! And you have come to spend Holy Week with me again," said the old man with a chuckle. "My! How big you are! You're almost up to my shoulder."

"I'm getting big," said Joseph. "Don't you think I'm big enough this year to stay up and see the priest light the Easter candle?"

"I didn't think of that," said his grandfather. "You always help me take it to church, but you have never seen the priest light it."

"Please let me go with you Saturday night," said Joseph. "I can stay awake."

"We shall see," said the old man with a twinkle in his eye. "It is a long time until Saturday. Come! Let me show you the candle I am making this year."

He led Joseph to the back of the shop. There on a marble table, lay a large plain candle. Joseph ran his finger along it. It was as smooth and soft as velvet.

"It will be very beautiful," said Joseph. "People say that you make the Easter candle more beautiful every year!"

"People are very kind," said the old man in a gentle voice. "Are you ready for some honey cakes and milk? After lunch you can watch me work on the candle."

When they had finished eating, his grandfather asked, "What did we put on the candle last year, Joseph?"

"First you put a white lamb on it, then some golden wheat, and then a cross," said Joseph.

"Very good," said his grandfather. "Come, let us work on the candle."

Joseph sat at the marble table and watched his grandfather work. "Grandfather, please take me to church with you Saturday night," he begged. "I will not fall asleep."

His grandfather did not say anything.

"Sister told us what happens," said Joseph. "At first, the church is dark. Then the priest strikes the new fire. After that the people light their small candles from the big candle. I want to be there and light my small candle."

Grandfather looked up from his work. "If I took you, you would be up very late. I don't think you can stay awake that long."

Joseph did not say any more.

For the next few days people came to the shop
to get their small candles for Saturday night.
Joseph waited on them and kept the shop clean.
Now and then he saw mice eating scraps of beeswax
that had dropped to the floor.

On Friday night as Joseph was getting ready
for bed, his grandfather said to him, "I'm going
out now. It will be late when I get back."

Before long, Joseph began to feel very sleepy.
"I guess Grandfather is right," he thought. "I
can't stay up very late."

He had just crawled into bed when he heard
a strange noise. Nibble, nibble, nibble! The
noise was coming from the workshop.

Joseph tiptoed to the door of the workshop. In the light of the moon he saw the candle. Then he saw two or three mice nibbling at the candle.

"Get out of here!" he shouted. He slapped the table with his hand and the mice ran.

"If I go back to bed," he thought, "the mice will come back. I had better sit up and keep them away."

It was late when his grandfather came home. Joseph was still watching the candle.

"It is a good thing you were here," said the old man. "Look at the broom. That is how the mice got on the table."

"Well, Joseph," he said. "You were able to stay awake to save the candle. I guess you will be able to stay awake to see the priest light it!"

Joseph went back to bed happy. His grandfather had said he could go to church Saturday night!

The next morning Joseph and his grandfather took the Easter candle to church.

That night they went to church early and knelt in a front pew. Joseph saw the priests and the servers come out to the altar. They went past him to the back of the church.

At last the lights in the church were put out.

"The priests will light a new fire and bless it at the door of the church," whispered his grandfather. "Then they will light the Easter candle with the new fire."

All of a sudden, light came from the back of the church and long shadows began to play on the walls. Joseph could not help turning around. He saw the priests and the servers bringing the Easter candle into the church.

They stopped three times. Each time one of
the priests sang something that Joseph did
not understand.

"What do those words mean?" he asked.

His grandfather whispered, "Sh! They mean
LIGHT OF CHRIST."

Soon it was Joseph's turn to light his small
candle from the new fire.

In no time at all everyone in church was holding
a lighted candle. The church glowed with light.
Joseph had never seen anything so beautiful.

As he held his candle, he prayed, "Oh, Jesus,
Light of the World, help me to see what is right.
Help me to do what is right. Take care of me as
I took care of Your candle."

Saul Becomes Paul

Saul lived at the same time as Jesus. He was
born in the city of Tarsus. As a young man, he
came from Tarsus to live in the land where
Jesus lived.

Saul did not have a last name. At that time,
most people did not use a last name. Sometimes
they were known by the city from which they came.
Sometimes they were known by the work they did.

When people asked Saul who he was, he would say,
"I am Saul of Tarsus. Some people call me Paul.
Someday they will call me Saul of Tarsus, the
tentmaker. I am learning to make tents."

Saul never met Jesus.

But after Jesus died on the cross, he heard
people talk about Him.

Some said, "Jesus was a friend of the people.
He taught people to be humble and pure and to
love one another. He made the deaf hear, the
lame walk, and the dead rise again."

Others said, "Jesus told the people that He
would start a new kingdom. He called Himself the
Son of God. That is why the leaders said He
sinned against God. That is why they put Him
to death."

"If He is dead," asked Saul, "why do people
talk about Him so much?"

"His friends are still teaching about Jesus,"
people told him. "They say that Jesus rose from
the dead. They say that He will come again to
rule heaven and earth."

"His friends are doing wrong," said Saul.
"They must be stopped. I want to help our
leaders stop them."

As he was on his way to see the leaders, Saul saw a mob coming down the street. The mob was dragging a young man with them. The young man's name was Stephen. Stephen had been teaching about Jesus.

Saul followed the mob. Just outside the city gate, some men laid their coats at his feet and asked him to watch them. Then the men threw stones at Stephen and killed him.

Saul, at this time, thought it was a good thing that the men killed Stephen. He thought that anyone who preached about Jesus should be put to death.

Saul went to see the high priest. "I want to help you fight the friends of Jesus," he said. "What can I do?"

"Here is a list of His friends," said the high priest. "Find them and bring them to me."

Then one day Saul heard that others were preaching about Jesus in a faraway city. He set out to bring them back to the high priest.

When he came near the city, a bright light suddenly flashed around him, and he was struck to the ground. At the same time, a voice said, "Saul, Saul, why do you fight Me?"

And Saul asked, "Who are You, Lord?"

And the voice said, "I am Jesus whom you are fighting."

And Saul trembled and asked, "Lord, what do You want me to do?"

"Rise up," said the voice, "and go into the city. There you will be told what to do."

133

Saul stood up. "I cannot see," he said. "Come help me!"

The men with him led him into the city. There he met a holy old man sent to him by Jesus.

The old man laid his hands upon Saul, and Saul could see. Then the old man said, "Come and be baptized. The Lord has chosen you to preach to all men."

From that time on, Saul was called by the name of Paul.

As Paul, he lived a long life and spent it preaching about Jesus. He went by land and sea to preach to many people.

He suffered much for Jesus. Three times he was wrecked at sea. Many times he was cast into prison. Once he was stoned. At last he was put to death at Rome.

Both Paul and Stephen are well-known saints of the Church.

Saint Gerard and the Loaves

"Today," said Father Crane, "I'm going to read
you a story. It is about Saint Gerard when he
was a little boy."

Ted raised his hand. "Father, is this a true
story or is it just a legend?" he asked.

"What do you mean by a legend?" asked Father.

"You told us that when we aren't sure that a
story is true, we call it a legend," said Ted.

"That is right," said Father Crane. "The story
I am going to read to you is a legend. It may
not be true."

Ted sat down, and Father Crane began to read.

Near a small town in Italy, there was a shrine
of our Blessed Mother. It was called the Shrine
of Our Lady of Graces.

It had a statue of our Blessed Mother holding
the Child Jesus in her arms. People from all
over Italy came to pray there.

Saint Gerard was born in this town. As a
small boy, he liked to visit the shrine. He
liked to go there to kneel and pray in front
of the statue.

He had been there many times with his mother
and sisters. But at the time our story takes
place, he had never been there by himself.

One day when he was about six years old, he
went to his mother.

"Mother, may I go to the shrine to see the
beautiful lady?" he asked. "I know the way.
I will not stay long."

"Yes, my son, you may go," said his mother.
"While you are there, be sure to pray for your
sisters and me."

It did not take Gerard long to get to the shrine. He opened the door and went in. The sun outside had been very bright. At first, everything inside the shrine seemed very dark.

Gerard waited a moment for his eyes to get used to the change of light. Then he went right up to the statue of the Blessed Mother and the Child Jesus and knelt down to pray.

As he began to pray, he looked up at the statue. He thought he saw the beautiful lady smile at him.

He blinked his eyes and looked more closely. He was sure now that the lady was smiling at him.

As Gerard watched, the beautiful lady bent down and placed the Child Jesus on the floor near him.

The Child Jesus and Gerard played just as all children like to do.

When they had played a while, Gerard said, "I told my mother that I would not stay long. I had better go now."

The Child Jesus gave Gerard a little loaf of white bread.

"Thank you," said Gerard. "I will be back tomorrow, if my mother will let me."

As Gerard was leaving, the beautiful lady
bent down and took the Child Jesus back into
her arms.

Hugging the loaf of bread, Gerard ran home
as fast as he could go.

"Look, Mother!" he cried. "Look what I have!"

"Where did you get it?" asked his mother in
surprise. She had never seen a loaf of bread
so white.

"The Child at the shrine gave it to me,"
he said. "The beautiful lady let us play
together today."

Every day Gerard begged his mother to let him
go to the shrine. And every day he would bring
back a little loaf of bread.

After a few days, Gerard's mother called his
sister Anna to her.

"Tomorrow, follow Gerard to the shrine,"
she said. "Find out who is giving him the little
loaves of bread."

The next morning Anna followed her brother to
the shrine. She hid behind the door and watched
what happened.

Anna could not get home fast enough to tell her
mother what she had seen.

"I saw the Blessed Mother bend down and put the
Child Jesus on the floor," she said as soon as she
could catch her breath. "I'm sure I saw the
Child Jesus give Gerard a loaf of bread."

"I'll go with you tomorrow," said her mother.
"I want to see this for myself."

The next day Anna and her mother followed
Gerard to the shrine. Everything happened again
just as before.

From then on, Gerard spent much of his time
at the shrine praying.

When Gerard grew up, he gave his life to God by becoming a brother. This means that he lived in a house with priests and brothers and worked for God. He was known as Brother Gerard.

One day one of his sisters went to visit him. She spoke about the white loaves of bread.

"Why don't you come home and visit the shrine?" she asked. "Maybe you will see Jesus again!"

"There is no need of that," he said. "I now find Jesus in everything I do."

Today he is known as Saint Gerard.

Father Crane closed the book. "Did you like this legend about Saint Gerard?" he asked.

"Yes," said everyone. "We liked it very much."

Saint Germaine

Long ago in a small village in France lived a little girl named Germaine.

She was not a pretty child. She was very ugly and sickly. Her hair was long and stringy. Her neck was full of sores.

Her stepmother kept her out of the house. She made her sleep in the barn. She would not let her eat with the other children, but threw her scraps left over from the family meal.

Yet Germaine was a very happy girl. She did not complain about her troubles. She said, "God wants me to suffer these things. This is my way to gain heaven."

In the early morning before the sun came up, Germaine would rise from her bed of straw. She would kneel and offer her day to God. Then she would lead her father's sheep up into the hills.

The sheep would eat the grass on the hillside.

Then, when the church bells rang for Mass, Germaine would fix her shepherd's staff in the ground. The sheep would gather around it. Then she would run down the hill, cross the brook, and go to Mass. The sheep would stay close to her staff until she returned.

In the evening as darkness began to fall, she would lead the sheep back to the barn. Then she would wait for the scraps of food left over from the family meal.

If she went near the house, her stepmother would scream, "Get out of here and stay in the barn. Don't come near us with your dirty sores!"

Never once did Germaine become angry, and never once did she talk back to anyone. She knew that God wanted her to suffer these things.

Before long, the people of the village began to talk about Germaine. "Look how the sheep stand around her shepherd's staff," they said. "They do not stray, and they are not harmed. It is a strange thing. Maybe Germaine is not the wicked girl that her stepmother says she is."

It was about this time that God began to show how pleased He was with little Germaine.

One day she led her sheep to the hillside. She heard the bells of the church ring for Mass. She fixed her staff in the ground, and the sheep gathered around it.

Then she ran down the hill to the brook to cross it and go to Mass.

But this morning there was a flood. The water in the brook was up to her shoulders. There was no way to get across to the church.

Some men from the village were working on the other side of the brook. They saw Germaine looking at it. They knew that she wanted to cross it to get to the church.

"Don't try to cross it today," they shouted to her. "It is too deep. You will be swept away by the water. You will be drowned."

But little Germaine blessed herself and began to cross the brook.

The men who were watching said that the brook stopped running, that a path opened up for her to cross.

As soon as she reached the other side, the men said, the waters closed again and the path disappeared.

The people saw many strange things happen in the life of little Germaine. They began to think of her as a saint.

One cold winter day, her stepmother saw her walking from the barn with something wrapped in her apron. Her stepmother thought that she was stealing food from the family to feed the poor.

She picked up a stick and ran after Germaine. It is said that as she raised the stick to strike her, Germaine's apron fell open. Out fell beautiful summer flowers.

Seeing summer flowers in winter surprised the stepmother. It made her think, and she began to see that Germaine was blessed by God.

Today, the Church calls her Saint Germaine. Her feast comes in June.